Kipper went into Chip's room and picked up the magic key. The key began to glow.

"Oh help!" said Kipper.

Kipper ran outside and looked for Biff
and Chip.

"Help!" he called. "The key is glowing."

Biff and Chip were playing with Wilf
and Wilma. They were playing in the
sandpit.

"Look at the magic key," called Kipper.

Biff was cross with Kipper.

"Come on everyone," she yelled. "Run inside. Get to the magic house."

It was too late. The magic began to
work. The children got smaller and smaller.

The children were in the grass and
everything looked big. The grass was like a
jungle.

"What big flowers!" said Kipper.

Chip saw a bumble-bee. He didn't like it and he didn't like the jungle.

"Let's get out of here," he called.

The children came out of the jungle.
They came to a mountain.
"What a big mountain!" said Wilf.

Chip began to climb. He wanted to get
to the top.

"Come on," he said. "Let's climb up."

The children got to the top. Kipper was hot.

"I don't like climbing mountains," he said.

The children looked at the sand.

"It looks like a desert," said Biff. "Let's go down."

"Oh no!" said Kipper.

"Look at the toy car," said Wilma. "Let's get inside and ride down. We can ride down to the desert."

Whoosh! The car took them down the mountain.

"This is fun," said Wilma.

The car stopped in the sand. The children climbed out.

"Oh no!" said Wilf. "Look at that big cat."

The children climbed inside a bottle.
Kipper was frightened.

"I don't like this," he said.

The cat looked inside the bottle. It
pushed it with its paw.

"Go away, cat," shouted Kipper.

"Shoo!" everyone yelled.

Floppy chased the cat away. The children climbed out of the bottle. "Good old Floppy!" said Biff.

They walked over the desert. Everyone
felt hot. Everyone felt very hot.
"I want a drink," said Kipper.

"Look!" said Wilf. "Giant strawberries!"
The children ran to eat them.
"I love strawberries," said Chip.
"So do I," said Wilf.

The children ate the strawberries. They pulled off big lumps. Kipper licked his lips. "I like this adventure now," he said.

It began to rain.

"What big drops!" said Wilma.

"I feel sick now," said Kipper.

"So do I," said Chip.

The children ran to a giant flowerpot.
They hid under it. The key began to glow.

The magic was over.

"I can't see," said Chip.

He had the flowerpot on his head.

"I like the hat," said Wilma.

Dad looked at his strawberries.

"I don't know," he said. "There must be giant slugs round here."